THIS BOOK BELONGS TO ....

SURPRISED

ANGRY

BORED

SLEEPY

SILLY

WEEPY

CHEERFUL

SAD

REC

DRAW THE VOLCANO EXPLODING.

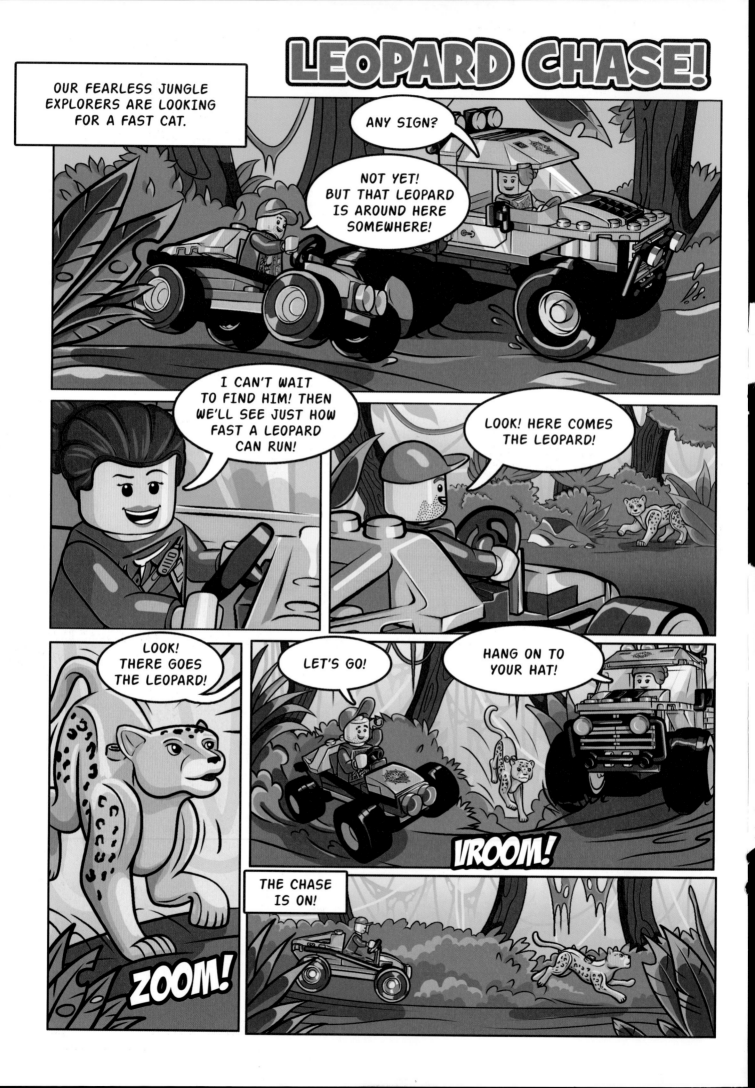

DRAW THE OCTOPUS'S TENTACLES TO STOP
ALL THE CROOKS, AND COLLECT ALL THE TREASURES!

WHERE ARE THE CRYSTALS?
DRAW THEM INSIDE
THE FALLING
LAVA PIECES!

HARD FLIGHT, SOFT LANDING

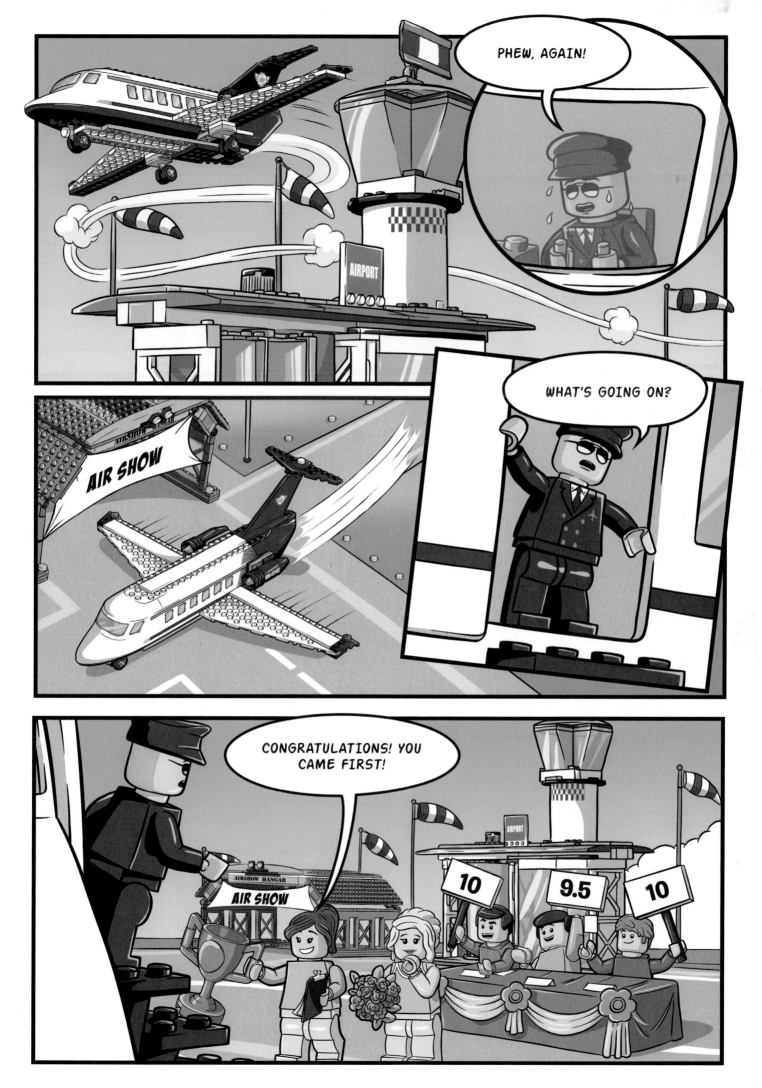

HOW TO BUILD THE FIREFIGHTER